The city lights and stars are bright,

so it's time to say goodnight

For Harpie.
Dedicated to everyone
who loves Nashville, and rightfully so.

Nashville is fortunate to have hundreds of amazing non-profits that work to make it an even greater place. A portion of the proceeds from every sale of this book will benefit one or more of those each month.

Copyright © 2016 by Jennifer Hillen

Harper Publishing, LLC
www.goodnight-nashville.com

ISBN: 978-0-578-17707-6

First Edition, 2016
Second Edition, 2017

Printed in the United States of America

GOODNIGHT, NASHVILLE

jennifer osland hillen

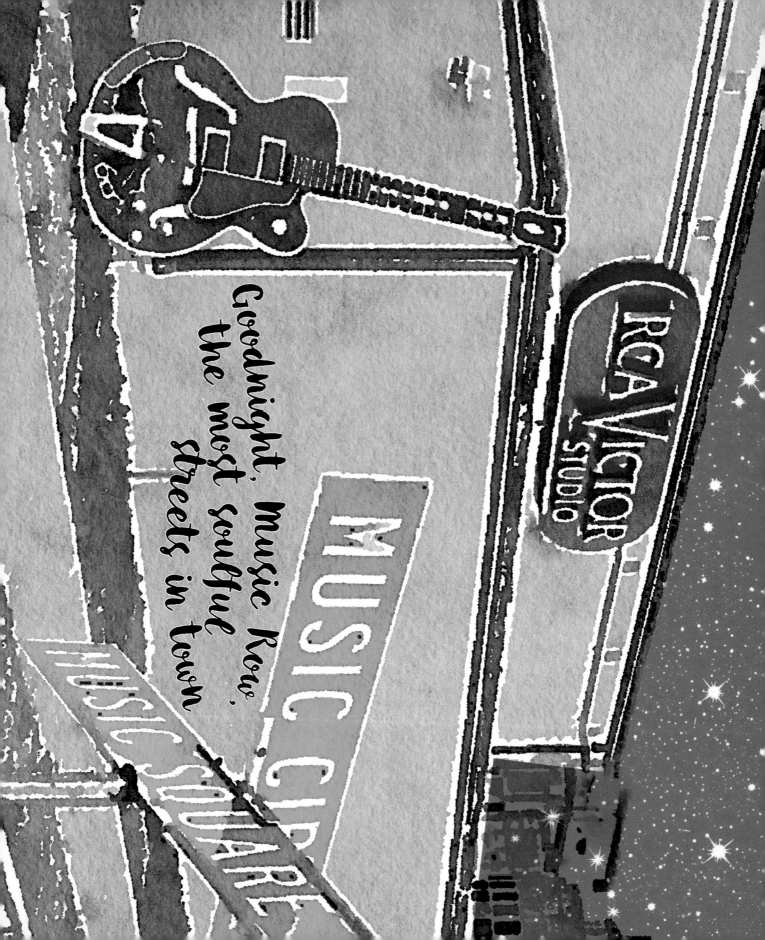

Goodnight, Music Row, the most soulful streets in town

Sweet dreams to all the artists making beautiful sounds

Goodnight to the Parthenon,
lit up in the dark

Sweet dreams, ducks, swimming in Centennial Park

Goodnight to the Ryman, the "mother Church" of music

Sweet dreams, General Jackson, hosting Cumberland cruises

Goodnight, Tennessee State Capitol,
sitting high above the city,

Sweet dreams to Percy Warner, with wooded parks so pretty

Goodnight to the honky-tonks that give our Broadway fame

Sweet dreams, Predators,
Titans and your games
we love to watch your games

Goodnight to the Bluebird,
where so many
get their break

The Bluebird Cafe

Sweet dreams to famous loveless.
with biscuits better than cake

Goodnight
Hatch Show Print,
with letterpresses
from way back

Sweet dreams to steeplechase, where strong horses run the track

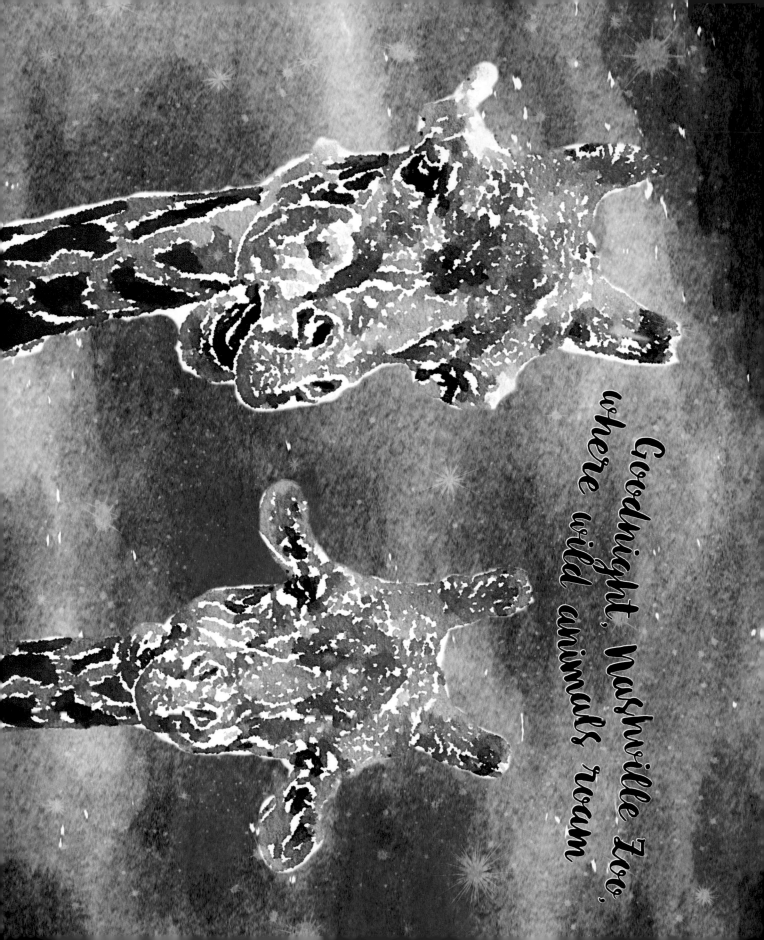

Goodnight, Nashville Zoo,
where wild animals roam,

Sweet dreams to the sounds,
where players run for home

Goodnight, Hot Chicken
and Goo Goo Clusters,
favorite tasty treats

Sweet dreams,
to The Tennessean,
you never miss a beat

Goodnight to our neighbors in historic downtown Franklin

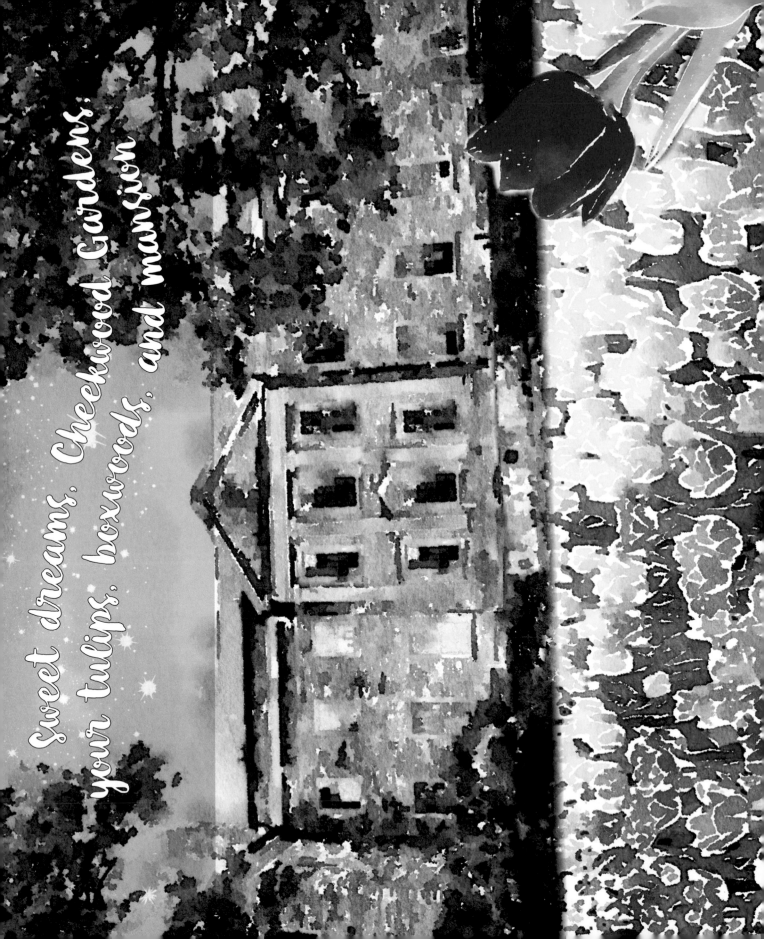

Sweet dreams, Cheekwood Gardens, your tulips, boxwoods, and mansion

Goodnight, Nashville Symphony, your stunning scores and space

Sweet dreams, Athens of the South,

and Radnor's scenic lake

Goodnight to
the Frist Center,
with colorful
art exhibits

Sweet dreams. Country Music Hall
of Fame. no one wants to miss it

Goodnight, Mr. Dragon,
watching over
The Belcourt Theatre

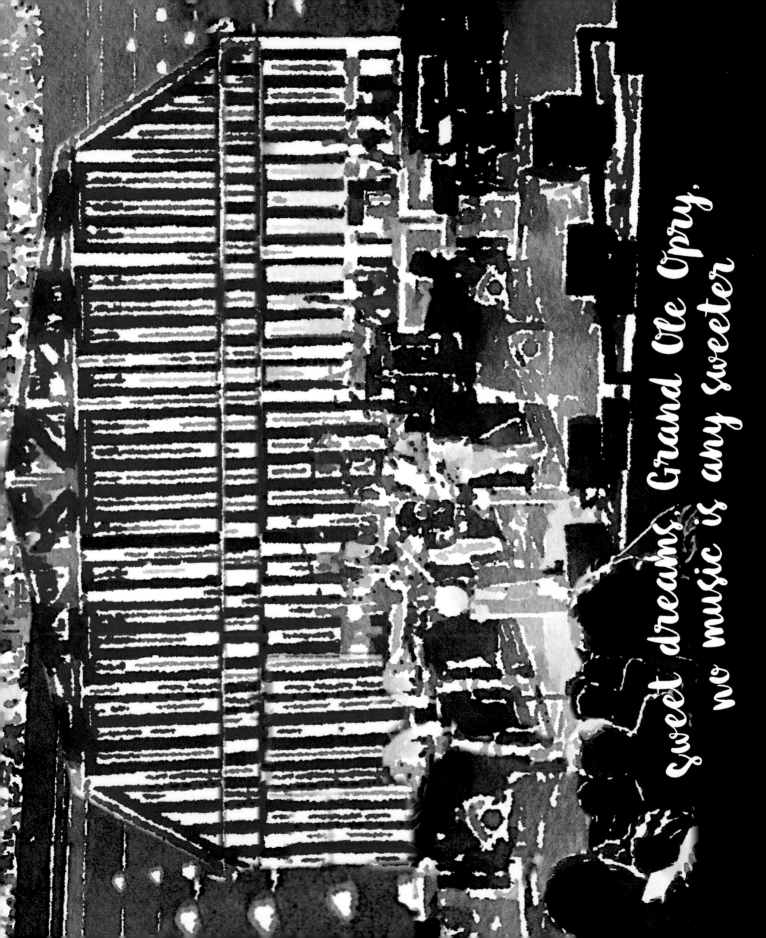

Sweet dreams, Grand Ole Opry,
no music is any sweeter

Goodnight, Nashville, those near and far, too.

Sweet dreams, Music City, we love you!

Jennifer Osland Hillen is a nearly-native Nashvillian, having grown up in the South and called Music City home for most of her adult life. Inspired by her beloved daughter, Harper, Jennifer had a special hope to honor, showcase, and give back to their amazing city. She is forever grateful to the family and friends who helped and encouraged her in writing and illustrating this debut book.

Visit www.goodnight-nashville.com for more information about this book as well as links to news, social media, and the author's other projects.

Pictured at right is an image of the hand-lettered ink and watercolor art print of the full text of *Goodnight, Nashville* commissioned by the author with local artist, Katie Cowan. Visit the above website for more.

Goodnight, readers.

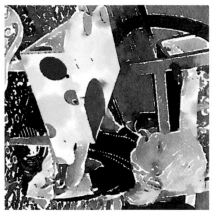